Jelly and Bean went for a jog.
They set off in the fog.

Oh no! They fell on a log!

'Get up and run,' said a frog.

Bean got up off the log.
Then he fell on the frog.

'Oh,' he said. 'I can't jog.

I will sit on the log.'

Jelly ran from the
fog.
She went to get a
big dog.

'Come on ... come on
... jog ... jog.
Bean is stuck in the
fog.'

The cat and dog ran
to the log.
They got to Bean and
the frog.

Jelly put Bean on the dog.
They left the frog in the fog.